LYME LOONIES

WRITTEN AND ILLUSTRATED BY DAVID SKIDMORE

First Edition

PAGE PUBLISHING, INC.
New York, NY

First originally published by Page Publishing, Inc. 2015

ISBN 978-1-68213-721-5 (pbk)
ISBN 978-1-63417-986-7 (digital)

Printed in the United States of America

DEDICATION

I dedicate this book to my wife, Sally; children, Flynn and Abby; father, Rod; and my extended family for their smarts, patience, support, inspiration, and love.

Furthermore, very close friends have been by my side through this hellish Lyme journey, so let me offer thanks to Cindy, Tom, Patrick, Katie, Nancy, Jenny, Doug, Lady of lyme: Christina, Cynthia, Tanya, Betty, Donna, Victoria, Cindi & Jessica, and Paula, and many more—you know who you are. You've helped me laugh, learn, share information; and you were simply there for me.

And, finally, to Sara, my partner in this book. Here's to Inanna House!

CONTENTS

INTRODUCTION

Things that make you go "hmmm." Life is either a comedy or tragedy. *Lyme Loonies* is a little bit of both.

I'm David Skidmore, creator of *Lyme Loonies.* I know there are many out there dealing with the misery, multisymptoms and mystery of Lyme. Something else I know is that a daily dose of comedy can bring laughter and hope to those suffering. *Lyme Loonies* is a series of cartoons that captures Lyme patients at their most vulnerable and desperate, while hanging on to their sense of humor. The cartoons are my way of expressing hope, humor, politics, and, yes, even revolt at the tug-of-war in which we find ourselves regarding funding, diagnosis, treatment, education, cure, prevention, and public apathy. I'm just writing and drawing about Lyme disease as I see it, hear it, and feel it. For almost five years, I have had this disease, every coinfection, and major neurological complications. Yes, I have all the goodies!

Let me stress that *Lyme Loonies* is not about making fun of those affected by the disease. I know firsthand the pain, suffering, and confusion that Lyme can cause.

The name *Lyme Loonies* was born when I first started creating the cartoons and pondered over a name for the series. Well, it just so happened that I read an article about a well-known doctor who was stepping down as head of research on Lyme with a federal organization. As he was bidding goodbye, he wrote a colleague, "I will certainly miss all of you people—the scientists, but not the Lyme loonies." Bingo! I thought, "Here is a doctor of significant power and influence regarding the current and future state of our health, a man who took the Hippocratic Oath to honor the profession of medicine and, specifically, to cause no harm." As I see it, this doctor's use of Lyme loonies was disparaging and caused a lot of harm both emotionally and scientifically. As a Lyme patient, I thought, "Wouldn't it make sense for our community to embrace Lyme loonies?" That was the remark that launched the *Lyme Loon*ies cartoons. He will see that name and know that we will not be diminished by a flippant phrase. We have embraced it as ours! Plus, what could be more loony than what we go through with this disease?

Lyme disease is controversial. No matter what side of the fence you're on regarding Lyme disease, treatment, coinfections, and chronic Lyme, I create cartoons in the spirit that we are human beings with families, coworkers, and friends; and many of us are holding on as best we can. So please don't make fun of us. Help us.

CHAPTER 1

Politics

Where does one even begin? We in the Lyme community know all too well the politics of Lyme disease. It would seem that as of late, some of the politicians are getting into the mix as well. That says a lot when these people who count on our votes are taking sides!

Here it is in a nutshell.

Little to no funding, no or little research on a federal level, inaccurate testing to the extent of 50 to 60 percent, many doctors treating Lyme disease having their licenses revoked, investigations into some of the government agencies, which have shown serious flaws, including undisclosed financial interests held by several of the most powerful IDSA panelists and individuals with financial interests in drug companies, Lyme disease diagnostic tests, patents, and consulting arrangements with insurance companies.

Long of the short, there are many issues surrounding this disease, given the lack of funding and or research and the fact that Lyme disease has now surpassed Aids/HIV and breast cancer patients, one would think that enough is enough. Certainly for those suffering and for those that will suffer.

> *In the fullness of time, the mainstream handling of Chronic Lyme disease will be viewed as one of the most shameful episodes in the history of medicine because elements of academic medicine, elements of Government and virtually the entire insurance industry have colluded to deny a disease. This has resulted in the needless suffering of many individuals who deteriorate and sometimes die for lack of timely application of treatment or denial of treatment beyond some arbitrary duration.*
>
> —Kenneth B. Liegner, MD

Help

According to the insurance company, CDC, and the IDSA watch, it's time to cut your Lyme treatment!
Skidmore

CDC Watch

I'VE GOT A GOOD JOKE FOR YOU!... LYME DISEASE!
HA HA HA HA HA
CDC
CDC
Skidmore

Big Joke

But it's Your Mother

Can't See You Anymore

You know...
we're going to
run out of paint
one of
these days!
LYME
Skidmore

Covering Up

Cracks in the Dam

Chronic Lyme, No Chronic Lyme

Damned Researchers

David and Goliath

It's Only Lyme Disease

Laughing Spirochetes

Lyme Gig

Lyme on Capitol Hill

Lyme at Window

Plum Island

Rally is Over

Relief Party

...Well you've come
to the right place for your
Lyme disease,
...Let's discuss your
treatment in here.
Skidmore

Sound Proof

Space Scanner

Throwing Weight Around

Zombies

Strong Support

Spirochete Find

Class, please take note... You never saw this!
INFECTIOUS DISEASE CLASS
Lyme Disease
Skidmore

Classroom

CHAPTER 2

Family and Patient Life

As they say, Lyme disease is multisymptomatic, as are the emotions for all involved. It is a disease that according to some doesn't exist. Vast amounts of money is spent on treatments, most of which insurance will not cover. People lose their jobs, their homes, their livelihood. Parents, children, even whole families can be affected.

How can something of this magnitude not affect all involved?

I can tell you firsthand it does, and although I make light because humor for me has been my shield, it is a sad affair. A lot of people are suffering from Lyme disease that don't have it. Thank you to friends and family for being there for us.

> *No one asks to get Lyme. It is a terrible illness that undermines your life and those of your loved ones. Hundreds of thousands, no, millions of people are sick with Lyme across the globe. Imagine the impact this is having on the global economy, as well as the emotional costs for those involved. Imagine the cost to society this is having.*
>
> —Mara Williams, RN, MSN, ANP-BC

> *Whether my husband failed the Lyme test or the test failed him may never be determined. Once you become a negative, you are relegated, dispossessed, invisible both personally and epidemiologically. You become the battle-ground of so-called medically unexplained symptoms, a pariah, medical mystery man, a conundrum, a reject, no-hoper, invalidated invalid, the dreaded heart-sink patient - that most hated of medical phenomena.*
>
> —Dr. Sandra Pearson Medical Director Lyme Disease Action, Psychiatrist

Airport Security

Bad Herx?

Breakthrough

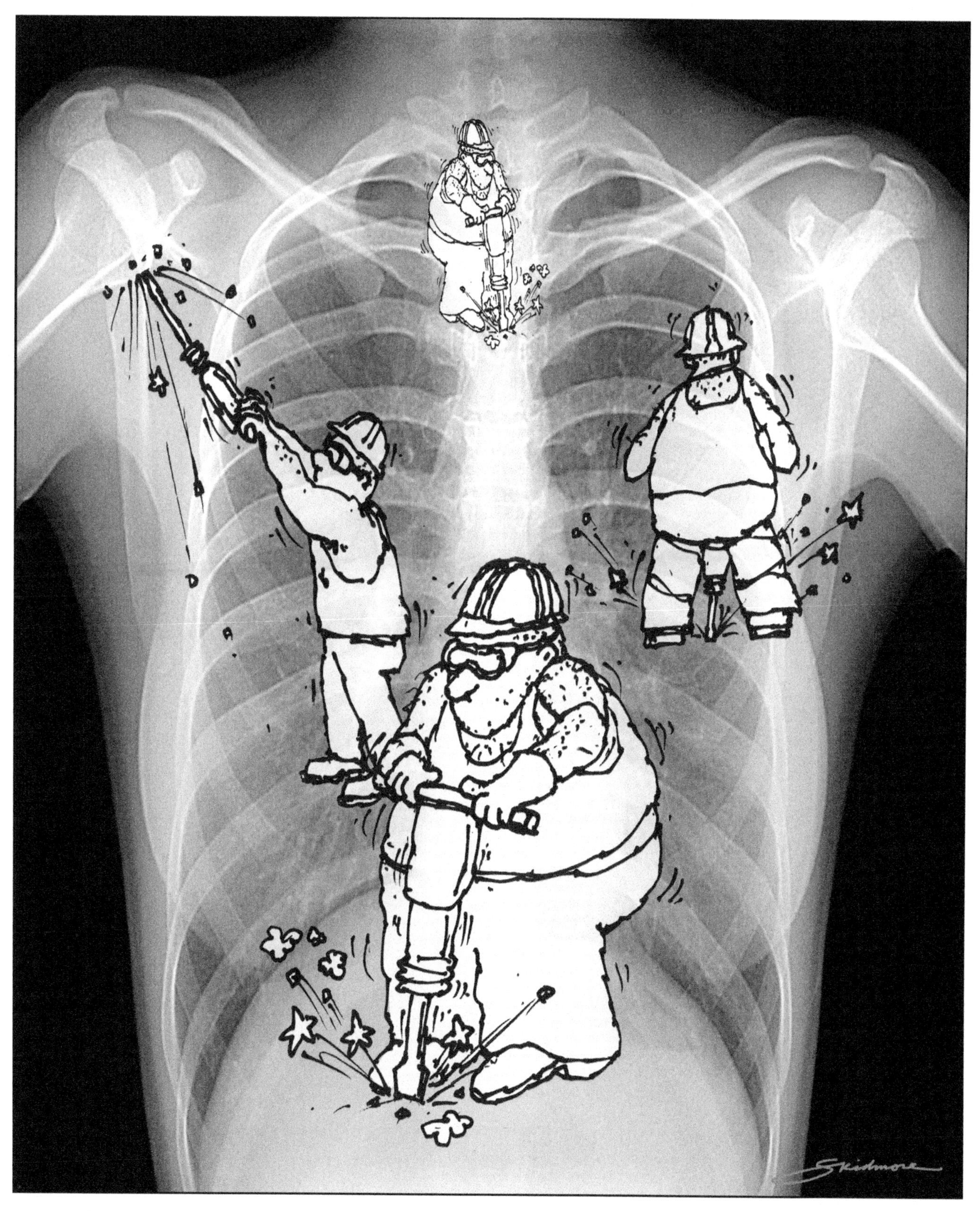

Chest X-Ray

Every Precaution

Getting Out

Holiday Cheer

Invisible Man

It's Lyme Time

Lyme Brain

Lyme Hell Ride

Lyme on My Mind

LYME RAGE

Good morning dear, I got you some orange juice.
...What the hell is that supposed to mean!?

Lyme Rage

I find these help to remember some of the more difficult things.
BRUSH TEETH
WALK DOG
MY NAME IS TOM
ADDRESS 205 MERTH ST.

Reminders

Lyme Zen

...Boy,
do I have a cold!
How about you
buddy?
Lyme disease.
DOCTORS
OFFICE

Lyme=$$$$$

Lyme Finances

Man Up!

May I Help You Ma'am

Normal

Not a Tick

Putting on a Good Face

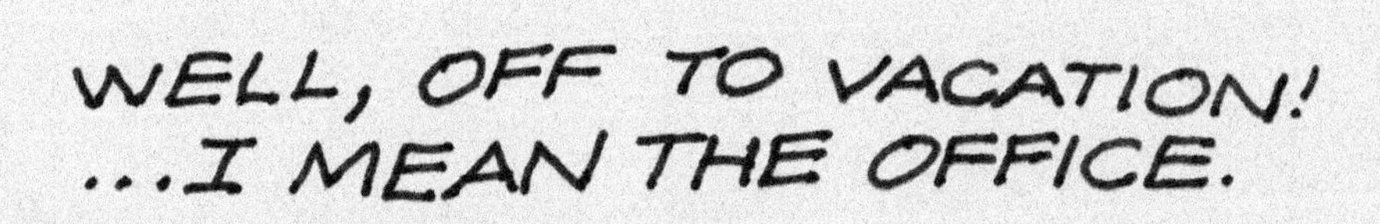

Vacation=Office

We Earn Stripes

You Look Fine

Think Positive

There's No Place

Something Serious

A LYME MOMENT

I'd like a menu.
...Oh, and I'll have a glass of water please.

Restaurant Lyme Moment

Read that Book

Misinformed

Lyme Fog

Looking for Something

If You Could See It

Airport Alarms

CHAPTER 3

Getting Treatment

If anyone told me of the horrors that lay before me regarding Lyme disease, there is a very good chance I never would have gone into the woods that November day . . . or at the very least, I would have worn a hazmat suit!

Unfortunately, for most, we do not learn about the hardships of this disease until we get it.

I gave it no real thought after I found the tick buried in the back of my arm. Seeing the telltale bull's-eye rash, I thought perhaps I should call my doctor. She ordered the standard three to four weeks of antibiotics. It was not enough. A little after three weeks, I began to get "flulike conditions." Fast forward to 2014, this is the longest case of the flu I ever had! In fact, it took almost two-and-a-half years, twenty-five to thirty different doctors, to finally hear Lyme disease. It was like the Fourth of July, and although I felt like crap, I was elated to hear it. Finally a diagnosis, little did I know it was just the beginning of the Lyme Hell Ride.

Although our stories may vary, we all share in regards to what we go through to find treatment. The testing for Lyme disease and the current guidelines for getting treatment are barbaric and from the dark ages, much like those that are calling the shots . . . I'm just saying!

I've already spoken of the cost, and I can tell you, it's a lot more than just monetary. Lyme affects everyone involved, in all aspects of life. All I can say is that if you don't have Lyme, make very sure you and your loved ones are properly educated and informed.

You Do Not Want Any Part of This!

Ok, now I know what I have; I have Lyme disease! Huh, that doesn't sound so serious; now I just need to get rid of it. Let me tell you… I had no idea.

—Daryl Hall

Persisters in Borrelia biofilm are like a bad day in the office, papers are flying, phones are ringing and still most of your colleagues are in deep sleep.

—Dr. Eva Sapi PhD.

Across the Border

All the Way From the Top

How did it go with the new Lyme doctor today?
...Fantastic!! he mixed all my meds and supplements into one pill!
Skidmore

Big Pill

WELL, IT IS A BULL'S EYE RASH... BUT WE HAVE ANOTHER COMPLICATION!
Skidmore

Bull's Eye

By Any Means Necessary

...CORRECT ME IF I'M WRONG, BUT ALL I SAID WAS YOU HAVE LYME DISEASE!?
Skidmore

Finding Out

Your garlic treatment isn't so bad
with this fan...
and your boss gave you your own office!
Skidmore

Garlic

Herxheimer Reaction

I'm Not a Believer

Not Your Doctor

Lots of Files

Lyme Pain Chart

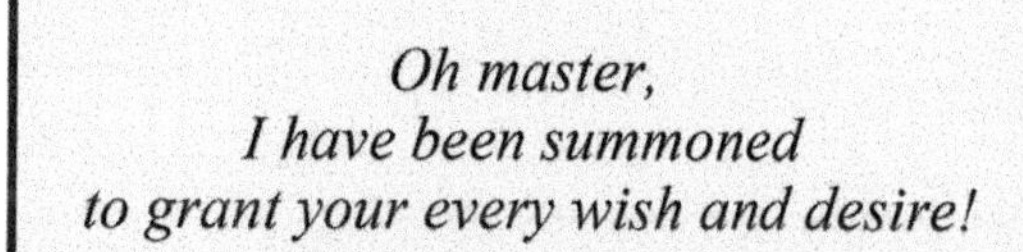

Not Even A Genie Can

Old Ones Back

Trust Fund Cure

Speaking Out of Both Sides of Their Head

Lyme Disease!?
...Rule number one residents,
...think inside the box!
Skidmore

Inside Box

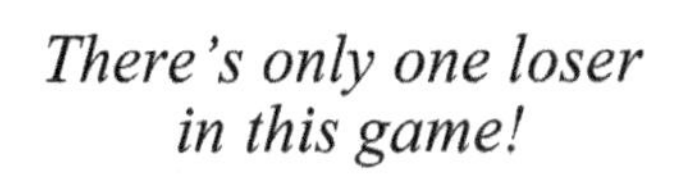

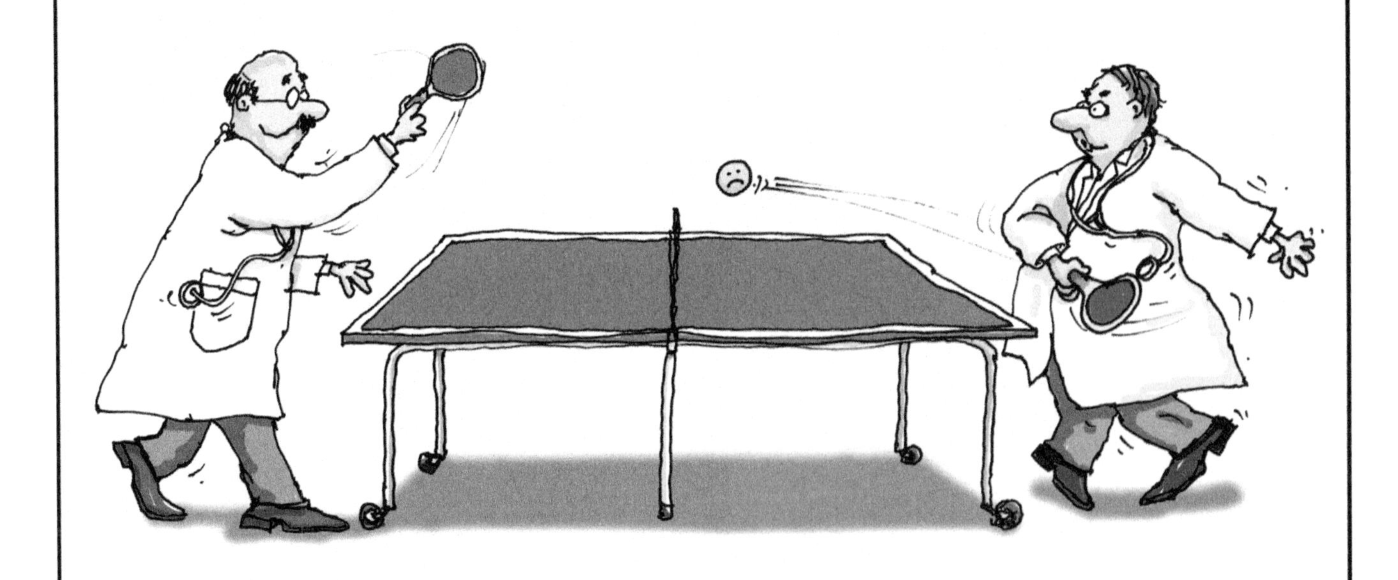

Doctor Ping-Pong

Couldn't Be

A Lyme Discovery

ARE THERE ANY RESTRICTIONS TO MY DIET FOR LYME DISEASE?
...YES, EVERYTHING!
Skidmore

Lyme Diet

Learning On Our Own

All in Your Head

Tijuana Trip

CHAPTER 4

Ticks

Ah, my true sense of humor, or to some, my lack of?

I, like most people with Lyme disease, cannot stand the thought of these little creatures. Although, I've always thought and said, creatures they are and they are doing what comes naturally.

It's the mess they leave after their meal that we could do without!

Actually, now that I think about it, and much like the cartoon I did of Noah throwing them overboard, we could indeed do without them. Shiver as you might, this, too, is part of my humor.

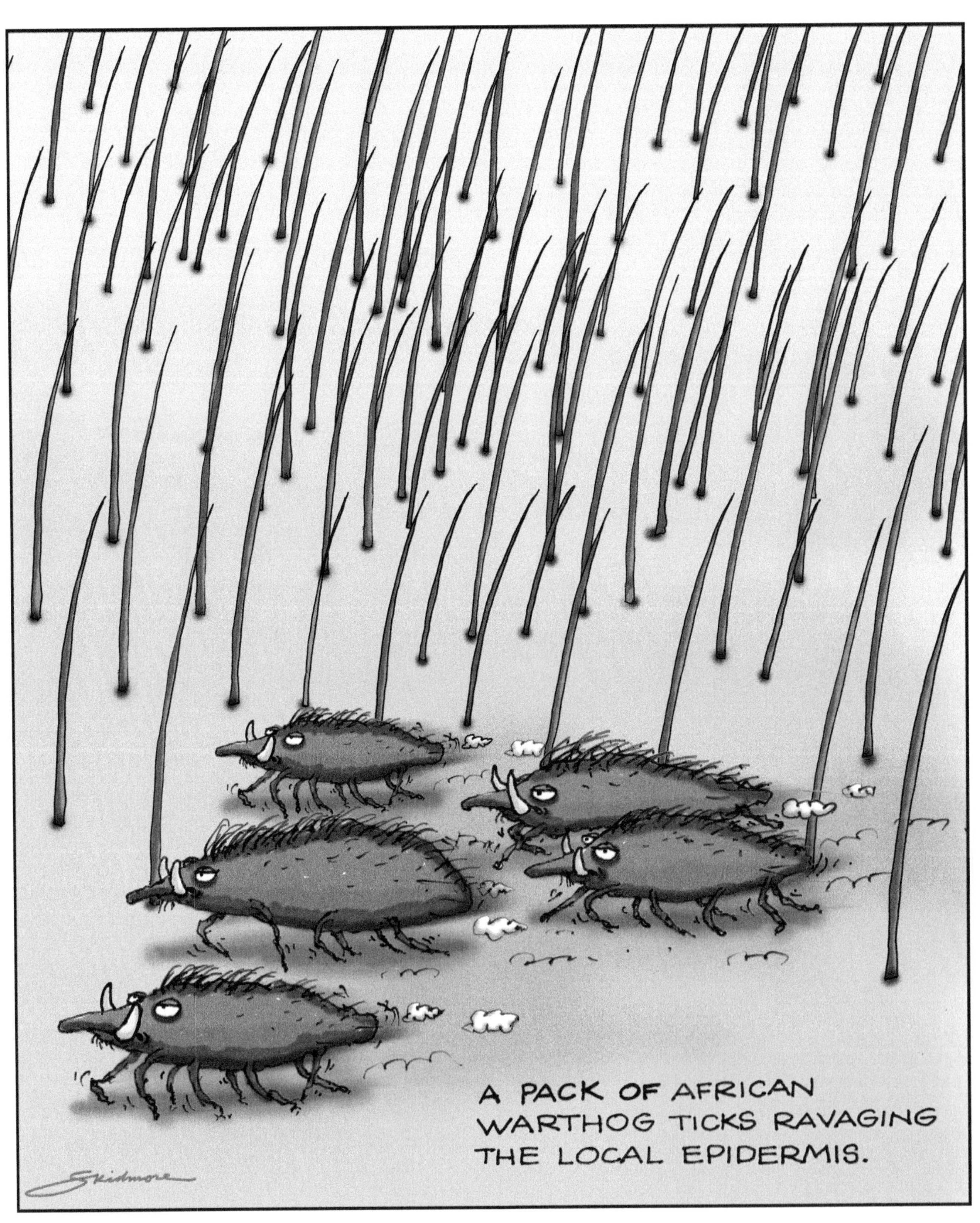

African Warthog Ticks

An Outing with Family

Identity Crisis

Sheepish

Snacking Before Dinner

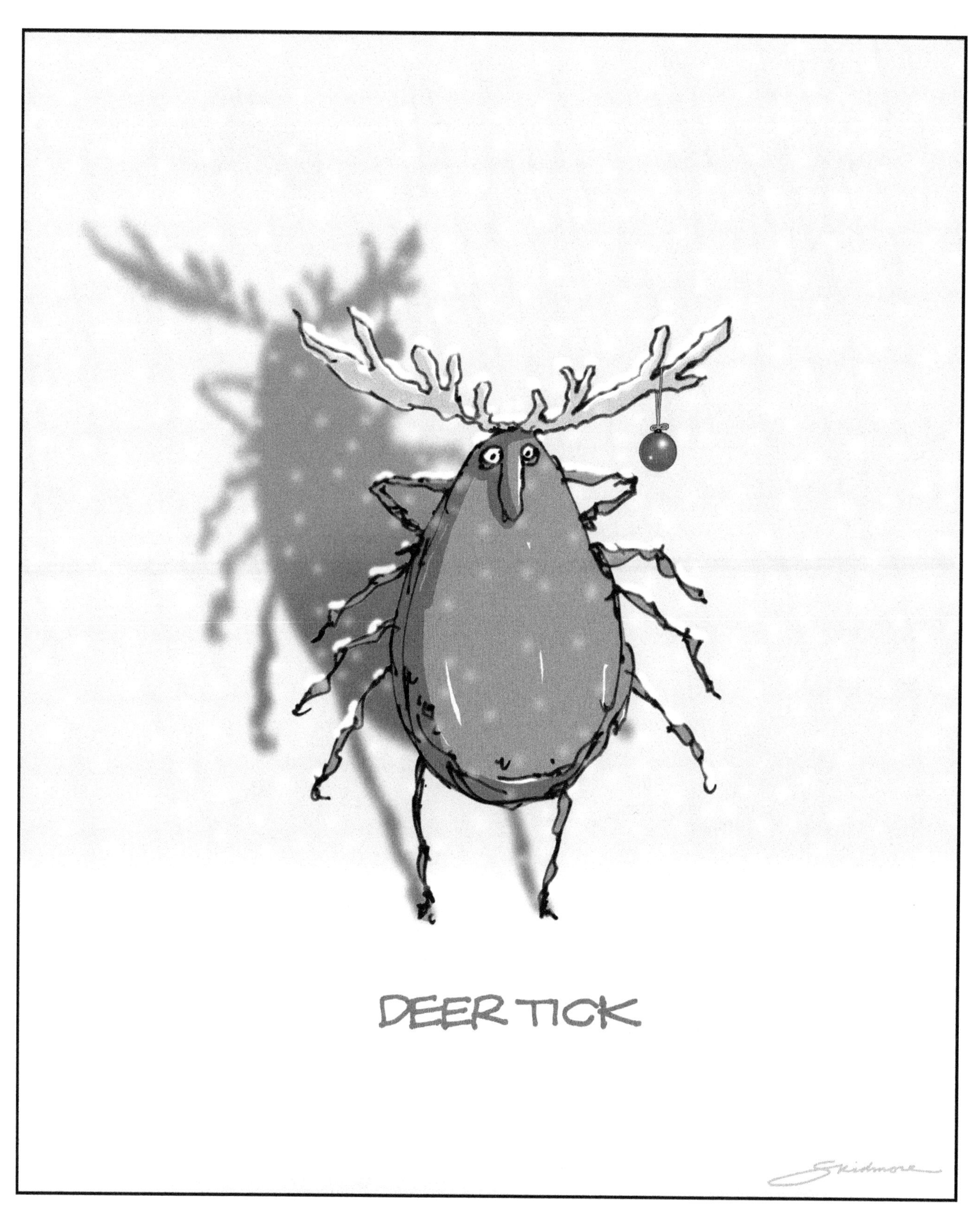

Species

Stick to Your Kind

Thank You Bob

They Must Not Catch On

Ticks on Vacation

There is only one thing worse than this Polar Vortex, short hair!

Winter Time

CHAPTER 5

Outdoors

Like so many of us, before Lyme, I loved anything to do with the outdoors. As I sit here and write, I can see the lakes, the mountains, and I can still hear a babbling brook.

I now watch with a tender heart all of the above, on television!

In actuality, during the last five years, I've gone fishing once with my father, brother, and son. I kept thinking, with every step I took, can one get Lyme on top of Lyme? The only place I felt safe was by a rock surrounded by moving water. Oh, but there were trees above me; could they get up that high and drop down? So now my love of the outdoors has been overshadowed by a creature the size of a pinhead!

> *I felt like I had the worst case of the flu every day, and then I was having trouble remembering things and making bad decisions. I was scared. I said to myself, "It's like I'm getting old before my time. Why is this happening?' I thought I'd had a stroke."*
>
> —Baseball Hall of Famer Tom Seaver

Tick Free Camping

Hiking on Stilts

It's a Beauty!

New Tick Repellant

Noah and Ticks

Prehistoric Ticks

Tick Season

Bringing Us Together

What Could Be Worse

Lyme Lawn

Liver and Ticks

God's Creatures

Elephants Don't Mess Around

Deserted Island

A Masterpiece

CHAPTER 6

What Now?

Lyme Loonies cartoons are about many things. They are about hope, holding on to a sense of humor, politics, and yes, even revolt given the tug-of-war we find ourselves in regarding funding, diagnosis, treatment, education, and/or a lack there of.

No matter what side of the fence you are on regarding Lyme disease, we are human beings, with parents, children, loved ones, and families, some of which are holding on as best they can.

Lyme Loonies is proud to donate 10 percent of the proceeds from this book to Inanna House—a planned in-patient integrative healing and resource center for people suffering from the effects of Chronic Lyme Disease (CLD) and other Tick-Borne Disease. The vision of Inanna House is to create a new paradigm of healing. This encompasses treating the whole person—including physical, emotional, spiritual, mental, and energetic aspects. The 501c3 organization is currently seeking to raise sufficient funds to build a pilot in-patient retreat center in Northern California. Payment for treatment will be based on a sliding-scale structure as treatment costs can be prohibitive for many patients. To learn more about Inanna House, donate, and get involved in the development of this groundbreaking center, please go to www.InannaHouse.org

ABOUT DAVID SKIDMORE

From early on, Brooklyn-native David Skidmore knew that making people laugh was a strong point. He could usually be found in the hallway drawing cartoons, playing music, and fooling about in class. After stints in the military, house restoration, and sign painting, he found his calling in advertising with a firm in the big apple. During an outdoor family excursion, David was sidelined by a little tick carrying a big disease. The effects on his body have been profound, but miraculously, he is still able to draw and make people laugh. He began *Lyme Loonies* to illustrate his frustrating journey in receiving a proper diagnosis and getting adequate treatment. He posted a few to Twitter, and the rest is history. David lives with his wife and two children in Brooklyn, working on his cartoons that have brought laughter and life to a community in need.

REFERENCES

Quote from Kenneth B. Leigner was taken from the internet, it has been passed around as a quote in many different Lyme circles. He originally wrote it in a letter to the IOM regarding Lyme Disease. Article can be found here: http://lymedisease.org/news/lymepolicywonk/554.html

Quotes by Mara Williams and Dr. Sandra Peterson and Dr. Eva Sapi were used with permission.

Quote by Daryl Hall was taken from an interview done on Healthline.com, you can find it here: http://www.healthline.com/health/daryl-hall-lyme-disease#2

Quote by Tom Seaver was taken from an article on nydailynews.com, you can find it here: http://www.nydailynews.com/sports/baseball/mets/madden-tom-nearing-terrific-day-mets-legend-winning-battle-lyme-disease-article-1.1289293#commentpostform

ENDORSEMENTS

It takes real talent to get us to laugh at something as serious as Lyme disease. David Skidmore's cartoons do just that.

—John McPherson, Close to Home Cartoons

Just when the seriousness of Lyme disease with all its issues feels overwhelming and negative thoughts creep in, a new "Lyme Loonies" cartoon shows up an puts everything back in the right perspective.

—Holly Ahern, Associate professor of Microbiology

David Skidmore captures the heartbreak, comedy and injustice of Lyme disease as no one else does or can. Bravo, David!

—Mary Beth Pfeiffer, Poughkeepsie Journal

CPSIA information can be obtained
at www.ICGtesting.com
Printed in the USA
BVOW07s2357140716
455386BV00025B/177/P

9 781682 137215